STEEPLECHASE

SIMON AND SCHUSTER • NEW YORK • 1957

FIRST PRINTING

LIBRARY OF CONGRESS CATALOG CARD NUMBER: 57-13296
MANUFACTURED IN THE UNITED STATES OF AMERICA
PRINTED BY THE MURRAY PRINTING CO., FORGE VILLAGE, MASS.
BOUND BY H. WOLFF BOOK MANUFACTURING CO., INC., NEW YORK, N. Y.

"*It's the people downstairs again.*"

"Want to know something, Dad?"

6

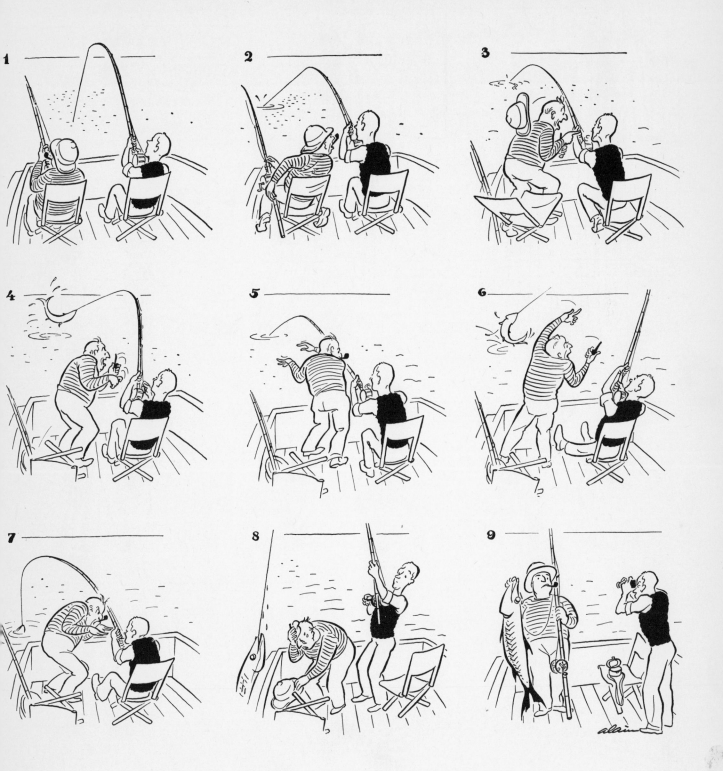

"Certainly I'm going to ask a question! Why do you think I had my hair done?"

"How was the cake?"

"It's a little fugue I wrote. I was hoping you might plug it at vespers."

7.

8.

9.

10.

11.

12.

15.

DONATED BY KIDDY-PANTS INC. MFG.

"*Still, did you ever stop to think where you and I would be if it <u>weren't</u> for evil?*"

"The old showoff!"

"Funny. I was under the impression that we had <u>seven</u> converts."

"*Don Catarino is going to Mexico City to have his tonsils out.*"

"Look, they __must__ be friendly, John! They raise children."

"You know, this stuff is like salted peanuts. Start eating it and you can't stop."

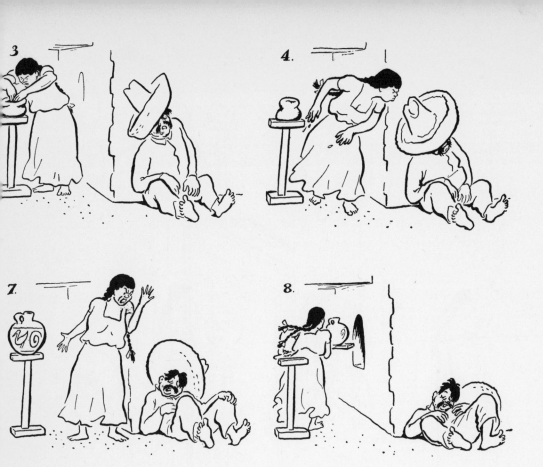

"*About how large a wall safe did you wish to hide?*"

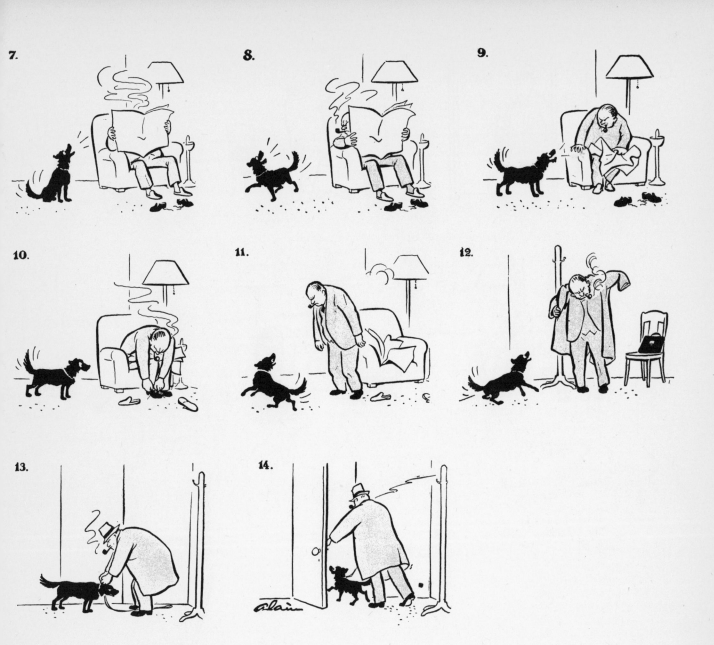

"Not for me, Pancho! I have to drive."

"Ask the padre. Maybe he knows what it's in honor of."

"This year I'm just giving everybody money."

"*Herbert, you'll be glad to know
that I have decided to raise your salary.*"

"I suppose in a few years all this will be done by atomic power."

PARKING
$ 50 for the first year
$ 10 for each year
thereafter

1.

2.

3.

4.

5.

6.

"I *played* on Notre Dame."

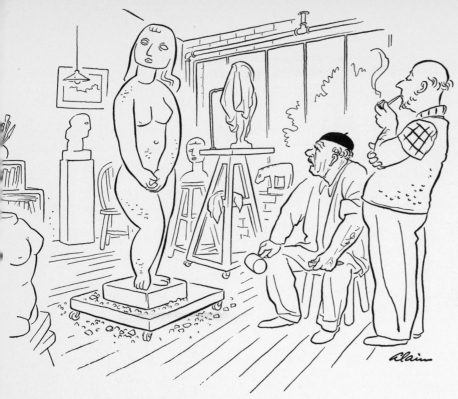

"Yes, the head _is_ too big. In the catalogue
I shall call it 'The Woman with the Large Head.'"

"Est-ce que je coupe la barbe de Monsieur Hammond?"
"Oui, vous coupez la barbe de Monsieur Hammond."

"Damn! I didn't bring any white."

1.

"I'll call Señor Diaz. He knows the stock better than I do."

"Oh, please, *please*, John! Don't you think you've said enough?"

"Do me one favor, will you—stop saying 'entre nous.'"

"We started out in a modest sort of way, making impartial tests for industry. Then, as time went on, we found that by making our tests a little less impartial . . ."

"We're trying out the honor system."

"Bungling fools!"

"Harry isn't in."

"My, I must look a fright!"

"You're *too* far back now, dear. Come forward a little."

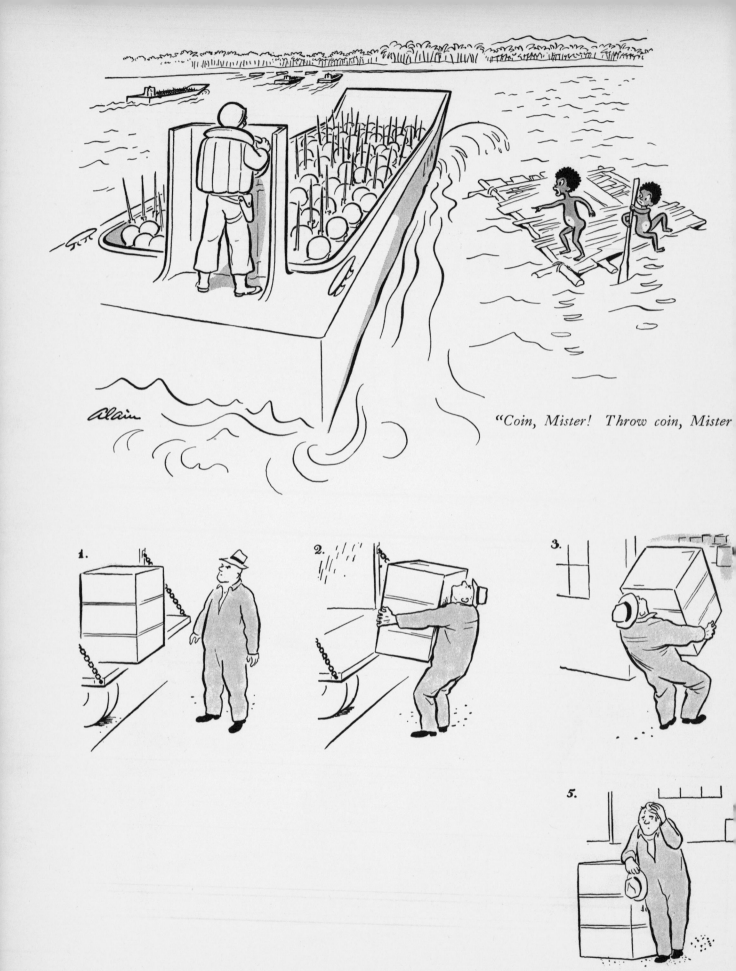

"Coin, Mister! Throw coin, Mister

"I didn't sleep a wink. Those cattle walked the floor all night."

"I've got to see Dr. Gallup. I've changed my mind."

"Don't just sit there doing nothing! Ask each other questions."

"I may seem old-fashioned, but do you have one with 'Welcome'?"

"By God, Mac—you were right!"

"He says, 'My house is your house.'"

"We're trying to determine the limit of human endurance."

"*I thought of cogwheels, of course. They're always good.*"

1.

2.

5.

6.

3.

4.

8.

1.

2.

3.

4.

"Big bird! Big bird come out of sky!"

5.

6.

"*Can you use us for atmosphere?*"

2. 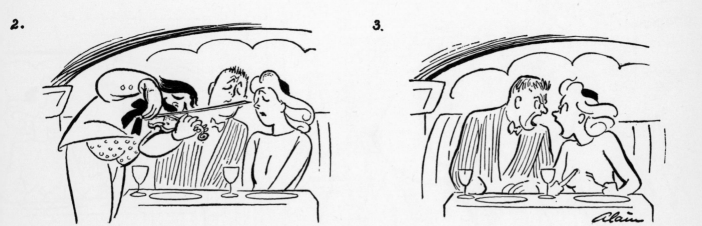 **3.**

"With or without?"

"I see Mugger McGuire is
going to be with us for the next few years."

"Here is your ticket to Mexico,
Madam. I know you will enjoy
it immensely.

If your trip affects you as
mine did . . .

you will never forget it."

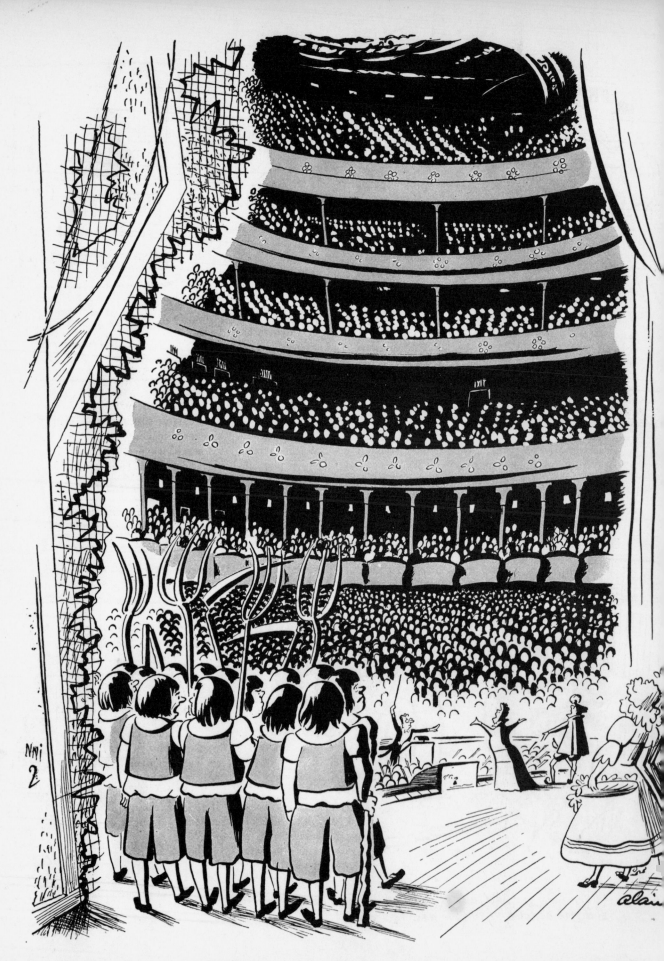

"Look at 'em out there! I'd like to see __my__ wife dragging me to this kind of a thing!"

"We're in for a __hell__ of a night. I've had experience with him before."

"*What makes me so damn mad is
the thought of that big order they gave us first.*"

"I think you'd enjoy 'Star and Garter,' sir. Excellent material for a sermon."

"One more question. That's real silver-blue mink, isn't it?"

...ink we can be congratulated on our foresight in voting ourselves these ...ases, thus assuring to the corporation our continuing loyal services."

"You always said you could lick him with your eyes closed. Now's your chance."

"*You can't exactly blame her—on a four-day cruise.*"

"*Sunday! I thought it was Saturday.*"

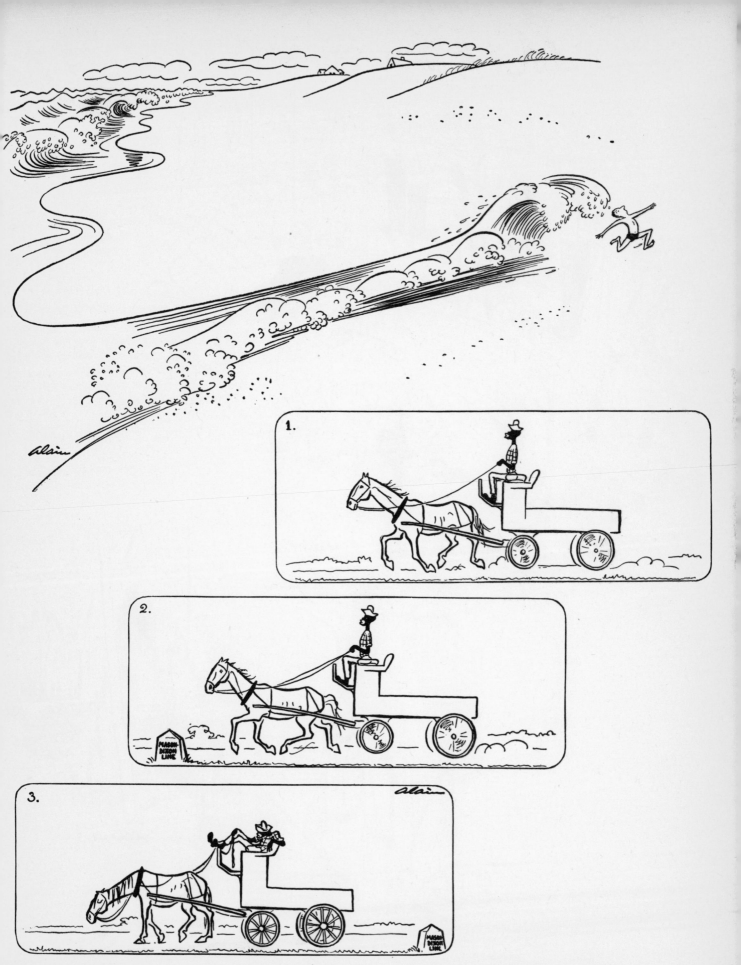

"I think my fees will seem less unreasonable to you if you will stop to consider the many long and costly years a doctor must spend to prepare himself, and the tremendous day-by-day expenses a doctor has to face . . ."

"Now, can you just hold this pose?"

"Don't interrupt, Henry. I'm only allowed fifteen minutes."

"That's my cousin José. He has insomnia."

"Good morning, gentlemen.   Check your house for termites?"

"Any ideas for a sermon, sugar?"

"His system has only one flaw—
it doesn't give him time
to place a bet."

"I don't like his holier-than-thou attitude."

"...and now let us pray silently for a moment that certain long-overdue repairs will be made to the rectory."

"*Suppose you let _me_ do the thinking around here.*"

"Insomnia, Johnson?"

*"No, he was a perfect gentleman. He just ran out of gas
and we __both__ had to walk back."*

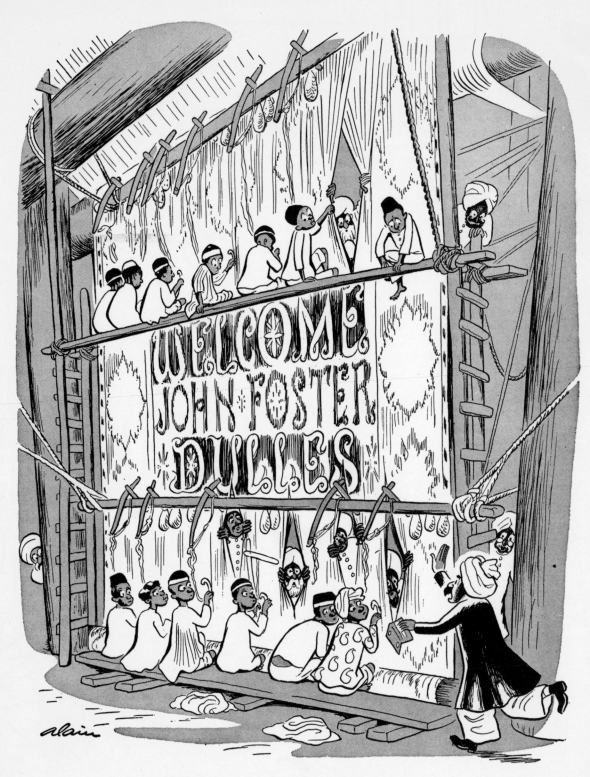

"Hold it! He's changed his itinerary."

"Hmm. Have Fulton's accounts been gone over lately?"

"Here I am, dear. Been waiting long?"

"From these eternal hills my spirit rapt
Its never-failing draughts of color drinks,
Nor knows what pageantry . . ."

1.

2.

3.

"It's all right, Ronald. I
felt it coming a long time ago."

"Well, well! I can remember when all they gave you was your quarterly interest."

1.

2.

4.

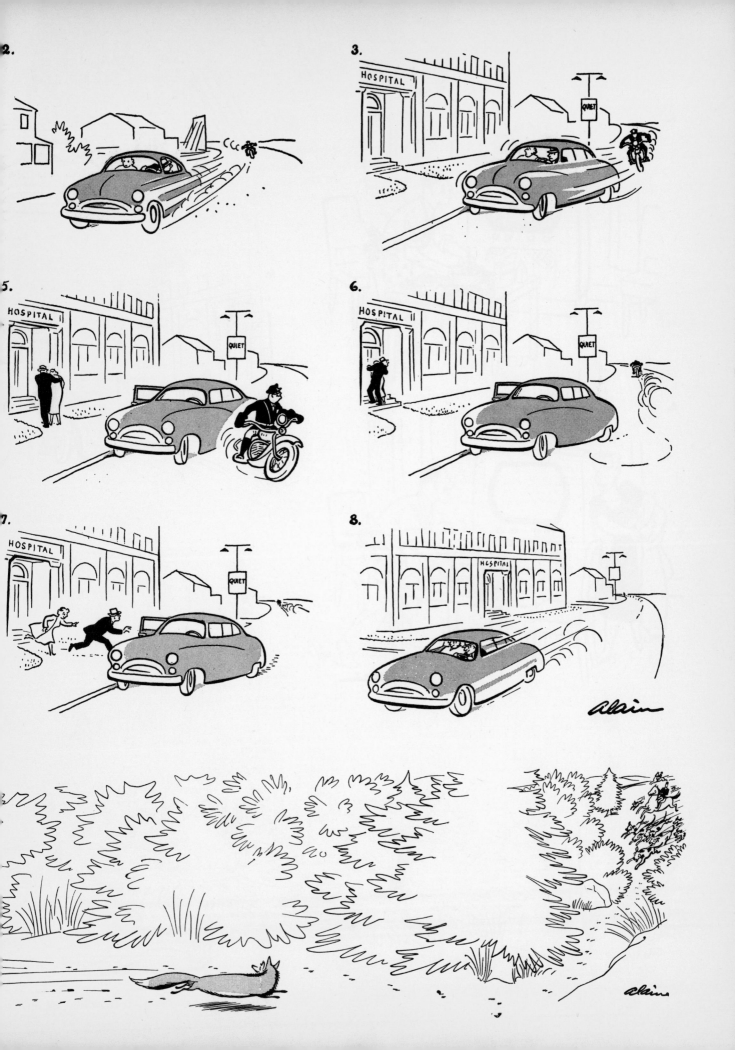

"Oh—not chop suey again!"

"It's a cozy little Dutch Colonial cottage with a tiled roof just down the hill from Vine Lane about half a mile after you pass the schoolhouse on River Road. She says you can't miss it."

"Sometimes I wish the rate of exchange _wasn't_ so much in our favor."

"I like your looks, Ramsey. You're hired."

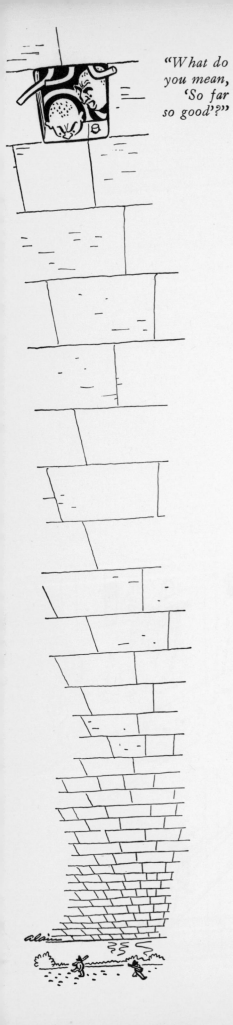

"What do you mean, 'So far so good'?"

1.

2.

3.

4.

"Here I am, Manuel. I'll take it on this window."

"I don't know how to break it to Tucker. He's being killed off in tomorrow's episode."

"And when you knock him down, go to a neutral corner."

"*Mon cher Monsieur from Armentières, par-r-lez vous . . .*"

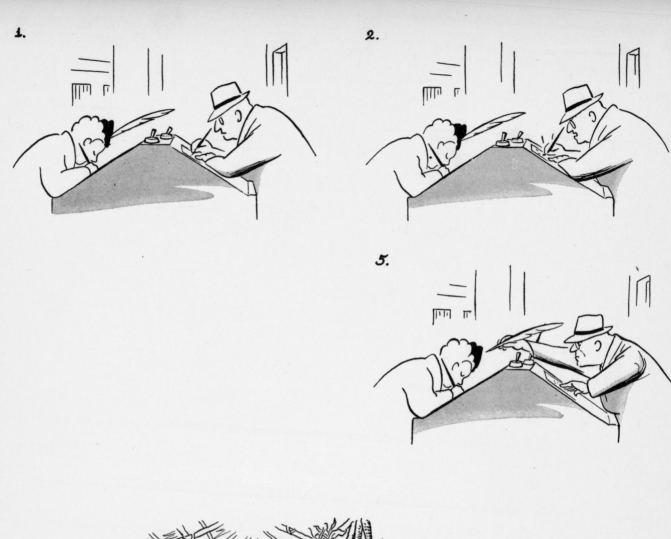

"*He says if we take the place, we'll have to buy the furniture.*"

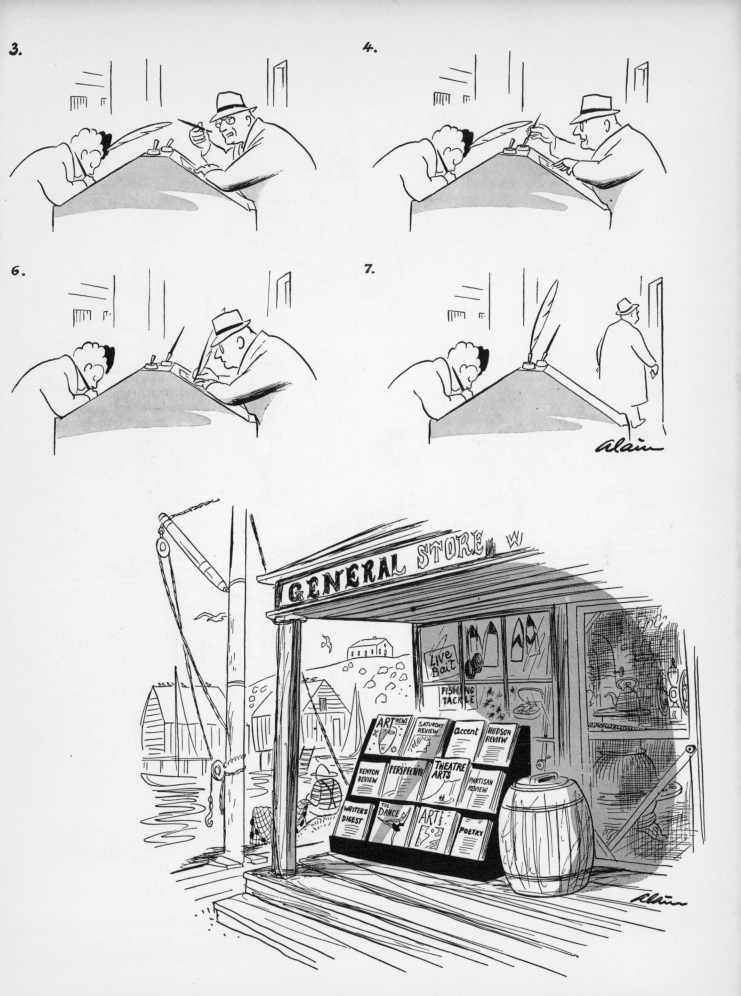

99

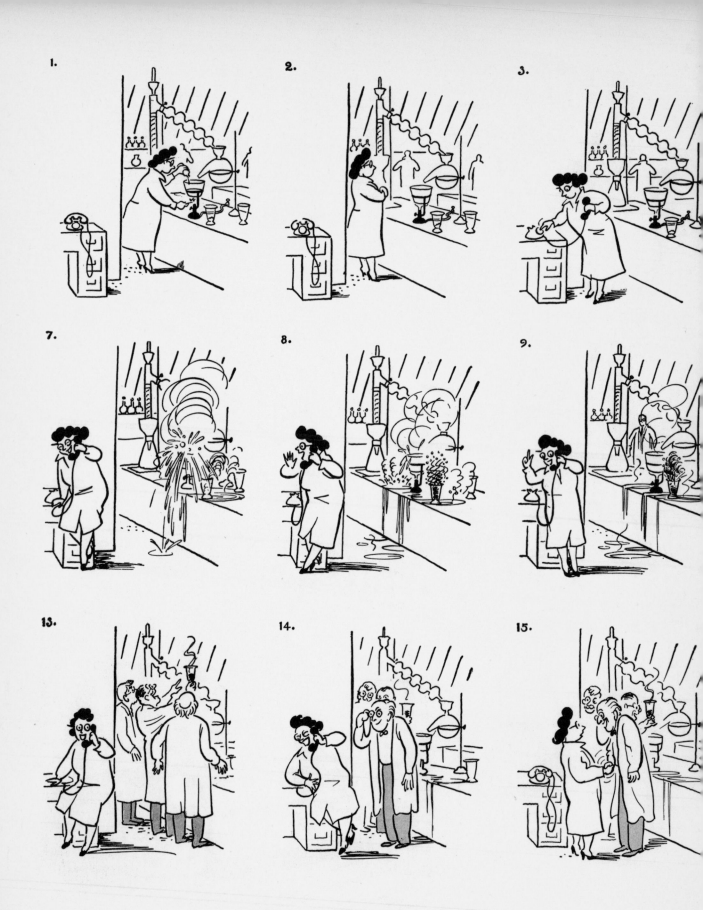

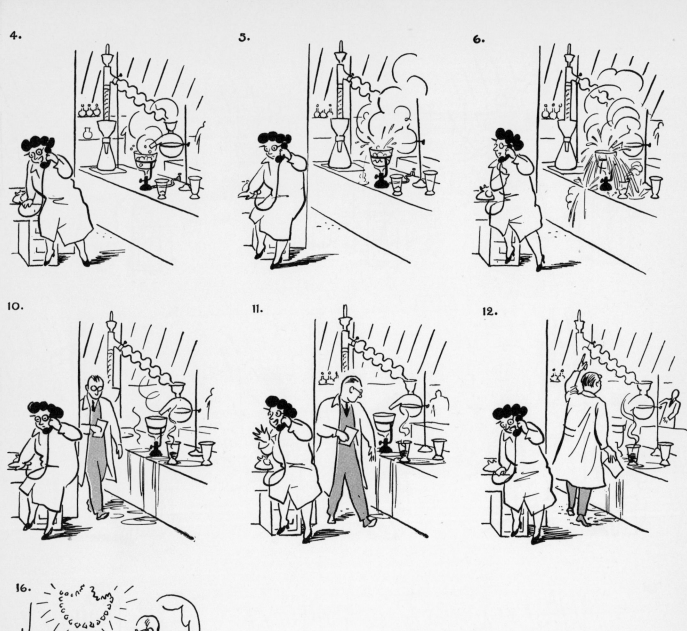

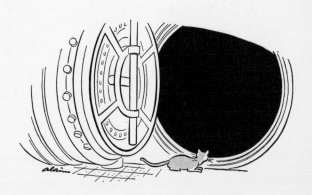

"Why the hell can't you watch where you're going?"

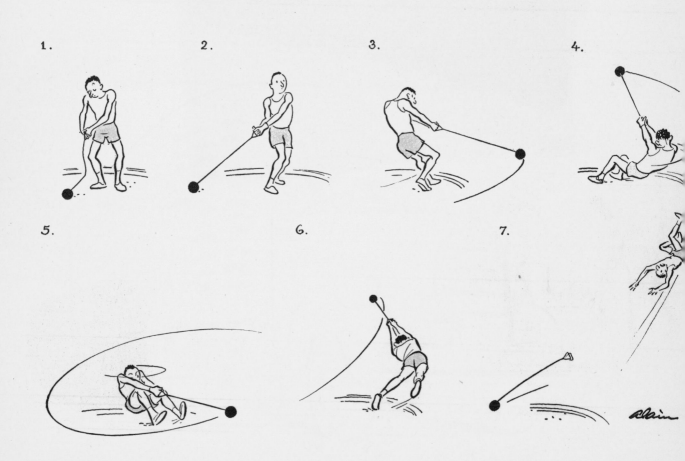

1.   2.   3.   4.

5.   6.   7.

"Halt! . . . Please."

"Try to make this one picture you don't cut the heads off in!"

"But ten paces will take me right into that poison ivy!"

"*But by now he would be gray.*"

"Got the towel?"

"You'll just have to wait. This table is for six."

"Abdul is trying to forget women."

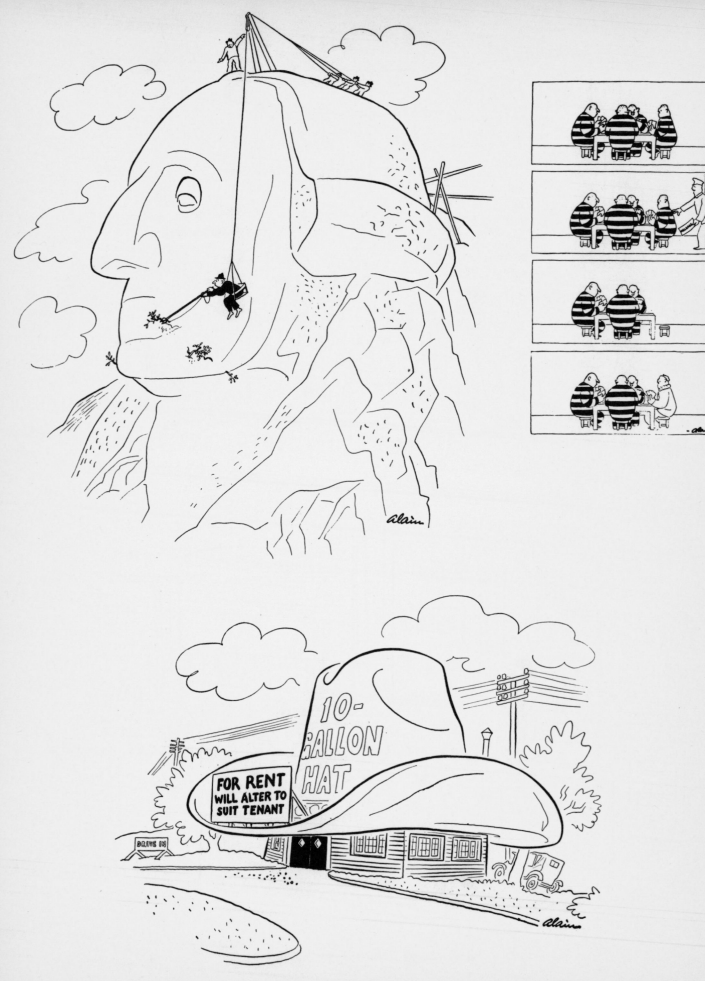

"Just thump it for resonance, sir."

"How does *that* thing work?"

"I'm sure she'll simply adore it,
sir—and here's the slip she'll need to exchange it."

"Now, this car was owned by a middle-aged gentleman who never drove it over one hundred miles an hour."

"This, friends, is my last broadcast for Strobalene. I've just received notice that my contract has been cancelled. I'd like to say in closing that this is typical of the Strobalene approach—hasty, arbitrary, completely without concern for others. And heaven knows what harm their cheap lubricant does to your car."

"*I'm not promising anything, mind you, but there's just a bare chance I can get you in the Futurity.*"

"*Try it on, Fred. See how it looks on you.*"

"A, Q, J, M, Z, O, R, W, P, I, N, B, C, L, E, X, T, R, D, G, U,
S, V, K, F, H, A, Y, M, T, V, A, N, Z, B, Y, C, P, L, X, D, W,
F, G, J, C, E, H, Q, R, Y, B, I, L, N, T, V, U. Allied Printing
Trades Council, Union Label, New York."

"It's a request program. Our audience voted for
fifteen minutes of absolute silence."

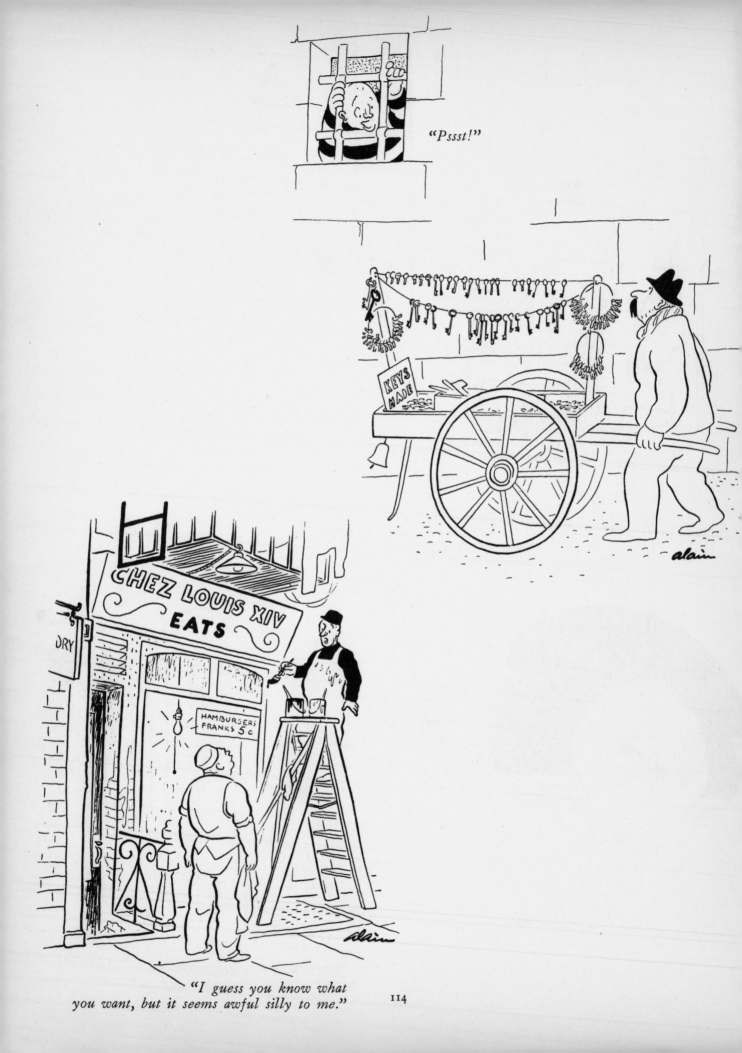

"Pssst!"

"I guess you know what
you want, but it seems awful silly to me."

114

"See that little knob on the top left? Turn that to 50. Now look at the ring on the front—the one with the green line on it. Turn that so the line points to f11. Now look at the next ring—it's got a little red line. Turn that to . . ."

"My idea is to consolidate my debts and have just one outfit hounding me.'

1.

2.

3.

4.

5.

6.

7.

8.

"*And yet they still go right on writing them.*"

"I have nothing to say."

"How's business?"
"Oh, about the same."

6.

7.

"Do you mind?"

"There! Now are you convinced that we're being followed?"

"My, you *do* have a green thumb!"

"Haló, Mamacita."

"Old Man Connelly has
been having considerable success with his ambush defence."

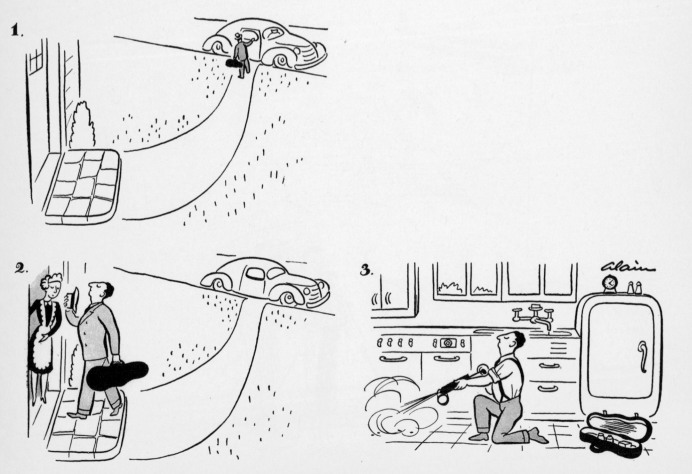

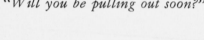

"Will you be pulling out soon?"

"*That will be all for today, thank you, Miss Spitzer.*"